Naked Retirement

Living A Happy, Healthy, & Connected Retirement

By Robert S. Laura

Published by Spirits Publishing For The Retirement Project

RetirementProject.org

Editor: Tim Drexler

Copyright 2010 Robert S. Laura

Printed in the United States of America

ISBN 10: 0-9754250-7-2

ISBN 13: 978-0-9754250-7-7

Robert S. Laura—2nd ed

Naked Retirement

Published by Spiritis Publishing Brighton MI
RetirementProject.org

RetirementProject.org

<u>Dedication</u>

This book would not be possible without the love and support of my best friend and amazing wife Amie and our beautiful children.

I love you Amie, Connor, Ava, Lucas, and Drake.
Words cannot express what you mean to me!

Contents

Foreword

Buck-naked. That was the image emblazoned in my mind. Not the typical image one associates with retirement, but nonetheless, the image that stuck when I heard the title of Bob's guide; *Naked Retirement*. Understand, though, this wasn't an image of sandy beaches or smoky men's clubs, this was the image from Hans Christian Anderson's ***The Emperor's New Clothes***.

In case you've forgotten the fable, rascally men wove a tale (pun intended) of a very special cloth made from very special thread. The king would spare no expense in having a suit made of this thread – threads which he believed could be seen only by those who were wise and worthy. There was, of course, no special thread. And the king did not recognize his stupidity (and public nudity) until it was too late.

As you'll read in the pages that follow, it is only the recent generations, guided by Wall Street profiteers and Madison Avenue marketers, which have been sold an idea of the perfectly dressed retirement. It's the retirement portrayed in brochures of happy, healthy retirees who achieved their sexy silver-haired good looks by investing in mutual funds and buying annuities. (I assume you know, most of the retirees pictured are professional models, not fellow retirees)

When, on Monday October 15, 2007, Kathleen Casey-Kirschling became the first "baby boomer" to file for Social Security benefits, the retirement industry already knew there were 80 million more just like her preparing for retirement in the coming decades. As a financial planner, I preach the power of planning- a personal and dynamic process contrary to the dust catching tomes called "Financial Plans" which rest on many shelves. And I believe in avoiding financial products whose processes can't be understand by the investors and whose fees aren't easily explained on a single bottom line.

Naked Retirement helps its readers embrace a simple process for approaching and planning for those years an industry has labeled "retirement." *Naked Retirement* causes the reader to stop and ask questions whose answers have no dollar signs nor life expectancy calculations. It requires those who desire a successful retirement to strip bare any preconceived notions of what retirement should be. Naked Retirement's premise isn't about wealth, it's about awareness. And there is nothing which makes one more aware than utter and absolute nakedness.

D. Drummond Osborn, CFP®
Personal finance columnist
Co-Founder, The Retirement Project
Partner, SYNERGOS Financial Group / OSBORN Wealth Management

Introduction

Naked Retirement was written to change the way people have been trained to think about and plan for retirement. It offers specific steps and exercises that transform retirement planning from a dollars-and-cents based approach to a new method that makes it more personal and meaningful. As the following story illustrates, taking a few extra steps like those outlined in this book can go a long way in making sure your retirement turns out to be everything you want it to be.

> *"One morning a volunteer named Ron showed up for his shift with his favorite lunch, leftover stew. No one knew for sure what was in it, but he was excited beyond description about it.*
>
> *When lunchtime finally arrived, Ron walked his prized stew to the microwave like he was carrying a new born baby. Having turned a plastic butter tub into his personal Tupperware for the day, Ron gently put his container of stew into the microwave, pressed Start, and began to whistle and tap his toes like he didn't have a care in the world.*
>
> *Three minutes later he cracked open the container, expecting to inhale the sweet scent of homemade stew. That's when there was a loud thud. Ron had unexpectedly chucked his precious lunch into the garbage and was walking away, visibly upset. "What are you doing?" asked some co-workers. Sadly, shaking his head, Ron said, "I grabbed the wrong container this morning and just microwaved an entire tub of butter." The lunch room erupted in laughter and for his next several shifts other volunteers and staff called him "butterfingers."*

It's a classic story that makes me laugh every time I read it, and it also illustrates an important lesson for new and soon-to-be retirees. Obviously, Ron could have done some very simple things to prevent this problem and ensure that he didn't end up with a container of melted butter for lunch. However, his own assumptions, thoughts, and actions blinded him to the situation … until lunchtime provided a heartbreaking dose of reality. Unfortunately, the same can happen to people if they enter retirement without a plan that prepares them for the mental, social, physical, and spiritual aspects of it.

Too often, traditional retirement plans are packed full of dollar signs, financial charts, and graphs. Leaving little to no guidance for people to deal with the everyday aspects of it. Therefore, as you read through *Naked Retirement*, I hope you can envision retirement planning in a new and more personal way… one where the words and actions focus on you instead of your money. Specifically, you will:

☑ Learn how to turn an average retirement into a time of life that is truly meaningful

☑ Avoid the dark side of retirement

☑ Answer the three most powerful retirement questions that will change your life in retirement forever

☑ Prepare for important conversations about your transition into retirement that will both strengthen your relationships and eliminate assumptions that can later turn into arguments

☑ Build a retirement "curious list" and a "friend list;" both of which will help you replace your work identity, fill your time and keep you connected to family and friends

☑ Create a one-page, inspirational *Naked Retirement* plan

Today's realities say it's time to step out of the box and plan for retirement very differently from the way we've been programmed. *Naked Retirement* will help you discover and achieve the best of what's next. I assure you, the results will be revealing.

Chapter 1
Retirement Reality

Retirement Reality

T he current way Americans approach retirement planning needs to change dramatically. Retirement today is nothing like that experienced by our parents or grandparents. However, much of the thinking, beliefs, and techniques that people use to prepare for it have changed very little with the times.

Right now, almost 100% of traditional retirement planning is focused on the wrong things. That statement may come as a surprise since I'm a financial professional whose primary job is to make sure people understand how much they need to save, that they have the proper asset allocations, and to put strategies in place to ensure they don't run out of money. Yet, I have found that each one of those planning factors pale in comparison to running out of family, friends, good health, and other intangibles that too often aren't discussed let alone planned for.

Financial professionals have a unique position in the retirement planning process. We get to see, year-over-year, the actual transition and what people become or, in some cases don't become, once they retire. It's a million dollar view … seeing what retirement life is actually like, and understanding the essential steps individuals and couples need to take in order to make a successful switch from the work world to everyday life at home.

I came across this story several years ago which eloquently captures the ideas and philosophy I want you to understand and build upon as you read through *Naked Retirement*:

> *A retired grandfather was preparing to watch his grandchildren while his daughter went to work. He was struggling to find the motivation and patience to make their time together enjoyable for everybody. His task was complicated by his grandson Bobby, who was constantly bored and couldn't stay focused on any one task for very long.*
>
> *The Grandfather tried several activities to engage Bobby, but none seemed to work. He was growing more and more frustrated until he picked up a magazine, flipping through it and found a brightly colored picture of the Earth. Pulling the page from the magazine, he ripped the picture into pieces and scattered them on the floor. "If you can put this puzzle back together," he told Bobby, "I'll give you a dollar." The grandfather returned to the other kids and began making lunch, assuming it would occupy Bobby for some time.*
>
> *Not even ten minutes later, Bobby walked into the kitchen, smiling ear-to-ear with the torn pieces taped together. The Grandfather was impressed to see that Bobby had finished so quickly, with all the pieces back in order. He asked his grandson, "How did you finish the puzzle so quickly?" "Easy!" Bobby replied. "There was a picture of a person on the other side so I just put a piece of paper on the floor, put the picture of the person back together, and then flipped it over. I figured if I got the person right, the world would be right, too!"*
>
> *The Grandfather laughed out loud, handed his grandson a dollar, and thanked him for the valuable life lesson: "If the person is right, the world will be right too."*

I believe there is great retirement wisdom in this story, highlighting the need and importance of making sure the individual is right, not just their asset allocation and account balance.

Retirement Reality

Securing a satisfying retirement in today's world requires different tools and ammunition than it did in he past. It calls for new and soon-to-be retirees to invest first and foremost in themselves. That means accepting the fact that for every hour invested in traditional retirement planning an equal amount of time should be spent on things such as replacing your work identity, establishing a healthy and active lifestyle, staying socially connected and involved, resolving relationship issues and concerns, as well as making the most of your God-given skills, talents, and wisdom.

In order for me to help you accomplish this I need you to trust the process I have created for you. As you will see, Naked Retirement contains a series of worksheets that we will be going through. Some are very fun and simple in nature while others have deeper meanings. In both cases, I want to emphasize the importance of completing the worksheets by actually writing down your thoughts, ideas, and beliefs.

What I know about retirement planning is that what we as individuals and couples choose to do and not do (what we write down and discuss and what we don't) can have a profound impact on the results we get. Therefore, I want to encourage you to make the most of the book by doing the work, and let me guide you toward amazing results in your both your personal life and retirement plans.

Now as you can see, the journey we are about to embark on is very different than any other retirement planning program. To illustrate this point, I typically begin my Naked Retirement workshops and webinars by asking people to stand up and share their name, how old they are, and how much money they have saved for retirement. Obviously, I can't do that in a book, but as you can imagine, the looks I get from people are hilarious. Some, get that nervous chuckle and look at a friend or spouse and say, "Is he serious?" Others panic and start to hyperventilate at the idea of disclosing their age let alone how much money they have saved.

It's a ton of fun to do with a group, but I don't do it for my own enjoyment. I use this approach to emphasize a very important point about my naked approach to retirement planning. Think for a moment, what do people typically say about age? That it's only a number and that it doesn't define who you are, right? Well, that is right! You see, even if I knew how old you were or how much money you had saved for retirement, it wouldn't change who you are or what you stand for. And that's the same logic that should be applied to retirement planning. It should not be defined by numbers and dollar signs alone.

That's why it's time to get naked: To shed all the financial figures and discover the best of what's next. Are you ready?

Get Creative

A couple planned to travel extensively in retirement. She retired from a major airline while he walked away from an automotive company.

So what was their creative retirement travel plan?

Her former employer offered retirees lifetime airfare for $50. She took a part-time job for a hotel chain, while he secured a part-time gig with a rental car agency.

Both provided deep discounts to employees in all of their favorite travel hot spots.

This represents a forward thinking approach that creates income, discounts, and most of all, the ability to achieve their retirement dreams.

Personal Reflections & Applications

Chapter 2

Retirement Perceptions

Retirement Perceptions

O ne of the biggest reasons people struggle to make a successful transition into retirement is because they rely on their own ability to understand and control it. Many pre-retirees create unrealistic expectations about how different and fulfilling it's going to be only to learn that their thoughts and desires don't exactly measure up. In fact, for many it doesn't even come close to what they hoped and mentally planned for it to be.

One researcher I spoke with stated that 75% of pre-retirees expect life in retirement to be better; but only 40% of actual retirees find that to be true. That's a major disconnect between perceptions and reality, and a fundamental reason why new and soon-to-be retirees need to open up their heart, mind, and eyes to the realities of everyday life in retirement.

I can share with you that my own perceptions about retirement were shattered early in my career. A friend asked if I would help him and his son on a remodeling project. In between the sounds of a saw and hammer, I said to my buddy, "It must be great being retired... to have the time, money, and freedom to come and help your son like this." He paused for a moment, looked me square in the eye, and said, "Bob, don't ever retire, because the minute you do, you won't mean anything to anyone anymore." Those were his exact words, "You won't mean anything to anyone anymore!"

Retirementality

"For to be free is not merely to cast off one's chains, but to live in a way that respects and enhances the freedom of others."

Nelson Mandela

"Be careful how you think; your life is shaped by your thoughts."

Proverbs 4:23 GNT

That's an awfully harsh statement for a retiree to make, especially since retirement is supposed to be the Promised Land, where alarm clocks and busy schedules don't exist and you're only accountable for your golf score, or being on time for your spa treatment. There was an obvious disconnect between how he thought life in retirement was going to be and what he was actually experiencing.

Too often, retirement is portrayed as the ultimate goal and sign of independence, but when people get there, it can feel very empty or hollow, in some cases, causing people to feeling isolated or unimportant. Primarily because many people are being told, and sold, the wrong message: That money and constant leisure are the keys to retirement and life-long freedom.

Yet, true freedom is anything but that. True freedom is void of fear, shame, guilt, and worry. It's knowing you're loved for who you are and loving others for what they are, and where they are at in life. It's an opportunity to be genuine and authentic... to live the life that God created you for.

That makes it important for new and soon-to-be retirees to take the time to think about and begin to plan for what everyday life in retirement is really going to be like. To figure out, what it will take to be happy, fulfilled and among the 40% mentioned above who find life is better without a boss or daily commute.

Retirement Perception Quiz
On the following page, is a fun and entertaining exercise that will challenge your perceptions about relationships, work-identity, daily routine, and physical wellbeing. Read the question and then circle one of the answer choices. Following the quiz, I'll explain the purpose behind each question and provide some examples to help steer your perceptions toward what life in retirement is really like.

RETIREMENT PERCEPTIONS QUIZ

Naked RETIREMENT

1. On your retirement cruise, you're left stranded on a deserted island. This is a big relief because you no longer have to deal with?
   a. Family member(s)
   b. Friend/relationship
   c. Money
   d. A specific commitment
   e. An impending decision you've been hesitant to make

2. A local organization is in desperate need of help. You're touched and call to offer one of the following items. Which one are you most likely to provide?
   a. Money, food and clothing
   b. Knowledge and other informational resources
   c. Personal skill
   d. Physical labor

3. To claim a $10,000 prize you must do one of the following. Which would you avoid at all costs?
   a. Eat vegan for an entire year
   b. Run a half-marathon
   c. Step onto a scale, in your swimsuit, on national TV
   d. Reveal an unhealthy habit or behavior on Dr. Phil
   e. I'm wouldn't avoid any - I'm a step above

4. A friend invites you to a party and upon arrival you realize your friend isn't there and you don't know a single soul. Do you?
   a. Scurry back to your car to wait for your friend
   b. Hide in a corner until your friend arrives
   c. Grab a plate and ask to sit with some strangers
   d. Seek out the host and introduce yourself

5. Some colleagues are talking about investments. Which would you suggest?
   a. High-yield dividend stocks, covered calls, and sector bets with Exchange Traded Funds
   b. They talk to your financial advisor
   c. Put half their money in CDs and the rest under their mattress
   d. Excuse yourself claiming a sudden need to use the restroom

6. Which one of the following is your biggest fear in retirement?
   a. Outliving your money
   b. Being ripped off
   c. Losing a loved one
   d. Losing your identity
   e. Health/healthcare
   f. Staying connected

Live Longer

Travel
Traveling keeps your mind active through new places and cultural experiences, physically fit through walking and climbing stairs, and is a great way to meet new people and make new friends.

Friends
According to a study at Flinders Univ. in Australia, people with an extensive networks of good friends and confidantes outlived those with the fewest friends by 22%.

Volunteer
According to a University of Michigan study, adults over 65 who volunteered at least 40 hours each year to a single cause were 40% more likely than non-volunteers to be alive at the end of study.

Prayer
According to the National Institutes of Health, people who pray daily are 40% less likely to have high blood pressure.

Question1 Overview: Stress

This is a powerful question because it shatters the perception that life in retirement is totally carefree and easy. It quickly and concisely pinpoints a major area of stress you may be carrying into retirement. Many soon-to-be retirees assume that problems or issues will just go away once they retire, but that's never the case. In fact, things can actually get worse because you will have more time to dwell on your problem, and fewer distractions to take your attention away from it.

Whether your answer pertains to a relationship, time commitment, or something financial, start resolving this issue now instead of dragging it with you into retirement. By resolving negative issues, you create space for more positive thoughts and feelings throughout retirement.

Question 2 Overview: Time & Identity

This question is designed to challenge the perception that every form of volunteering is fulfilling and effective in applying a person's work knowledge and skills. Many people plan to use some form of volunteering to help replace their work identity and fill their time. However, many retirees go into it with only general assumptions or vague thoughts about how their work skills will transfer and how rewarding, or in some cases, unfulfilling it may actually be.

For example, a woman retired from social work because she was burnt out from all the heartache and stress it caused her. After six months of retirement, she was bored and decided to put her people skills back to work by volunteering in - of all places - social work. Guess what? Within three months she was burnt out again … and this time she wasn't even getting paid for her added aggravation.

Then there was the retiring school administrator who planned to volunteer with Habitat For Humanity. Her intention was clear from the beginning. In her role at work, she felt as if nothing ever got finished. Whether it was curriculums or school policies, there was always something to update, review, or improve. Therefore, in retirement, she sought an opportunity to be a part of something that had definitive start and end dates, and a finished product to see and touch.

The difference between these two examples is that the administrator took the vagueness out of volunteering by having a specific purpose: Filling a void she experienced in her career, rather than simply acting out of boredom or trying to match old skills to new needs.

Question 3 Overview: Physical Health

This question confronts the idea that extra time and a more flexible schedule will provide motivation to exercise and eat healthier. Countless people say that's exactly what they are going to do when they retire but, it's not as easy as most people imagine simply because first we make our habits and then our habits make us.

Fact is, retirement does _not_ come with extra motivation, which is why its important to start taking care of your body right now and to acknowledge the short-comings you may have in this area of life. After all, more unstructured time at home can lead to more time in front of the fridge instead of on the treadmill.

It's also just as important for you to maintain strong mental health in retirement. That means making time for yourself as well as regular plans to have fun. Whether it's going to a comedy club, connecting with old friends, or volunteering at the local pre-school, making sure you find ways to stay amused is an important ingredient to a successful retirement.

Question 4 Overview: Social Style

Many people don't take the time to stop and consider their social situation during retirement. They don't realize that they'll be around fewer people than when they were working. For some, that difference is easily overcome; but it may be more difficult for others. Furthermore, God didn't create us to do life alone, otherwise He wouldn't have made Eve.

Therefore, as you approach retirement, make sure you are investing in others and cultivating relationships outside of the workplace. Being part of a group, regularly visiting with friends, and building new relationships are proven methods of increasing longevity and play an important role in fending off conditions such as depression.

Question 5 Overview: Money

There won't be much about financial matters in this book but, the reality is, people are more responsible for their retirement savings than ever before and shouldn't assume every investment or advisor is right for them.

It's essential that you can articulate the basics of money management and know at least some of the key questions to ask financial professionals in order to protect yourself against fraud, bad advice, or an investment scam. You don't need to become a financial guru, but I'll share the most important piece of financial advice that you will get out of this book. *No One Cares More About Your Money Than You!* Embrace that and your relationship with your money and financial advisor will change for the better.

Retiring Single?

You're not alone. Single people are now 96 million strong and make up 43 percent of the adult population. Three of every four single people age 65 or older are women.

Active Community
Consider living in an active community that has an activities director, whose job is to engage residents with one another.

The more activities and events there are, the greater your opportunities for staying involved.

New Best Friend
Make insurance your best friend. Consider disability insurance to protect your lifestyle and ability to save for retirement while working and then long-term care insurance to help pay for home care if you need help with your daily living needs.

Retirementality

"Even if you're on the right track, you'll get run over if you just sit there."

Will Rodgers

"Therefore do not worry about tomorrow, for tomorrow will worry about itself. Each day has enough trouble of its own."

Matthew 6:34 NIV

"When one door closes, another one opens but we often look so long and regretfully at the closed door that we fail to see the one that has opened for us."

Alexander Graham Bell

"Do not regret growing older. It is a privilege denied to many."

Unknown

"And in the end it's not the years in your life that count. It's the life in your years."

Abraham Lincoln

Question 6 Overview: Retirement Concerns

So much of retirement talk today is fear based. People are constantly bombarded with the idea that they are going to run out of money, be left alone, or suffer a debilitating medical condition. All of which are very real, but worrying about them will get you nowhere.

There's no doubt that you will face challenges throughout retirement, which is why you need to be proactive right now. Don't put your marriage, your friends, faith, personal well-being, or the need to secure the proper insurance on the backburner until you retire. Delay winds up getting in the way of living retirement to the fullest. Ask yourself, "What's one simple thing I can do to start addressing this fear today?"

Overall, your quiz answers represent the first step in helping you examine retirement in a more personal and less material way. One that is very different from the typical dollars-and-cents approach practiced by many.

The goal of this first exercise is to expand your thoughts and ideas about what retirement may actually look and feel like. To pinpoint areas of potential stress as well as highlight possible opportunities to maximize during your transition.

While this quiz is simple in nature, it's a prelude to a deeper, darker side of retirement that can affect those who don't have a plan to manage the mental, social, physical, and spiritual parts of it. Potential repercussion that can become major problems, temptations, or sources of conflict if they aren't addressed and planned for.

Personal Reflections & Applications

_____

_____

_____

_____

_____

_____

_____

_____

_____

_____

_____

_____

_____

_____

_____

_____

_____

_____

_____

_____

_____

_____

_____

Chapter 3

DARK SIDE OF RETIREMENT

DARK SIDE OF RETIREMENT

*R*etirement is often depicted as an idyllic life of leisure filled with contentment and joy. You might envision long walks on the beach, worldwide travel, quality time with family, or turning your memoirs into a NY Times bestseller, but retirement is just like every other phase of life. It can come with a dark side that's seldom discussed, and rarely planned for. One where the bondage of addiction, the hollowness of depression, and even the fiery depths of suicide consume retirees who aren't armed and prepared for the battles ahead.

This chapter came about after a casual conversation with a local doctor. After I outlined the premise of my book with him, I asked if there was anything he observed in retired patients that I might be missing. "One of the biggest issues with retirees," he said, "is addiction." Surprised, I asked him for more details and felt compelled to begin my own research.

I can tell you that I was stunned by what I discovered. There is a hidden epidemic taking place in the shadows of retirement that highlight the pressing need for individuals and families to prepare for much more than just the financial aspects of it.

A Chilling Prescription
It is expected that by 2020, the number of retirees with alcohol and other drug problems will leap 150% to 4.4 million – up from 1.7 million in 2001.

According to the Substance Abuse and Mental Health Services Administration, the proportion of older people treated for a combination of cocaine and alcohol abuse tripled between 1992 and 2008. For this group, in 2008, cocaine abuse was the leading cause of admissions involving drugs (26.2%), with abuse of prescription drugs a close second at 25.8%.

An Emotional Recession
The National Institutes of Health report that, of the 35 million Americans age 65 or older, about 2 million suffer from full-blown depression. Another 5 million suffer from less severe forms of the illness.

Women are at a greater risk for depression because of biological factors such as hormonal changes and the stress that comes with maintaining relationships or caring for loved ones or children who are ill.

Health conditions, including heart attack, stroke, hip fracture or macular degeneration, and procedures such as bypass surgery, can also trigger the onset of depression.

Depression is the single most significant risk factor for suicide among the elderly. Sadly, many of those who commit suicide did, in fact, reach out for help – 20% see a doctor on the day they die, 40% the same week and 70% the same month.

The Ultimate Crash
Suicide is the 11th leading cause of death in the United States, with an aggregate rate of 11 suicide deaths per 100,000 Americans. Suicide rates are highest among people over the age of 65, according to the American Association of Suicidology (AAS). That age group makes up 12.5% of the population and accounts for 15.9% of all suicides.

White men older than age 65 take their own life at almost triple the overall rate, and are eight times more likely to commit suicide than women in the same age group. Perhaps surprisingly, white men age 85 and older have the highest annual suicide rate of any group at 51.4 deaths per 100,000. In contrast, the rate among white women peaks between ages 45 and 64 at 7.8 deaths per 100,000.

As surprising as this information may seem, the threat of addiction, depression, and suicide becomes even more real as you examine their contributing factors. For example, baby boomers were the first generation to engage in the widespread use of recreational drugs, and the first group for which a wide variety of prescription medications were readily available and culturally accepted as treatment for nearly every ailment. They are also at a critical stage in life where stress can mount due to natural aging, bodily dysfunction, grief and loss, and the financial strain that often stems from caring for both aging parent(s) and adult children or grandchildren.

This shadowy downside of retirement appears to be exacerbated by the fact that today's seniors are from a generation that stressed self-reliance; a trait characterized by a reluctance to discuss financial and/or personal health matters. This attribute, reinforced by scientific research, suggests that contemporary seniors tend to blame themselves for their illnesses, don't want to be a burden on family, and worry that treatment will be too costly ... further evidence that life in retirement is like an iceberg, where 90% of what really takes place lies below the surface and out of mainstream conversations and retirement planning.

My goal for the remainder of the book will be to continue to guide you through exercises and questions that help you avoid the dark side of retirement as well as add purpose, meaning, and joy to the everyday things you do in the next phase of your life... starting with a useful twist on emergency savings.

Saving Grace Account
Most financial experts preach the importance of having a rainy day fund equal to 3-6 months of expenses to cover emergencies or unexpected costs. The same concept should be applied to your personal life in retirement. A Saving Grace Account cushions you when a challenge such as the loss of a loved one, financial hardship, an unforeseen medical diagnosis, or difficult decision leaves you vulnerable to the dark side of retirement. This support network can be just as important, if not more important, than a financial savings account.

Create a Saving Grace Account by listing your family, friends, professionals and organizations that you have a relationship with and can rely upon for help and support during emergencies and unexpected life events. Who do you turn to when times get tough or you're faced with a difficult situation? Who gets the first phone call when you're feeling down and need a pick me up? Who provides wise counsel or time-tested advice? Who has been there in the past when you needed help, a hug, or a kick in the behind? Who can and will pray for you? Who can you ask for financial support? Who would help you move into a retirement community, or nurse you back to health after a knee or hip replacement?

Personal Reflections & Applications

_____

_____

_____

_____

_____

_____

_____

_____

_____

_____

_____

_____

_____

_____

_____

_____

_____

_____

_____

_____

Chapter 4

RETIREMENT FOUNDATIONS

RETIREMENT FOUNDATIONS

Naked RETIREMENT

*T*raditional retirement planning typically includes a "visioning" or goal-based discussion that usually revolves around big picture items that require savings. For example, annual travel, a second home, or maintaining a lifestyle based on a percentage of your pre-retirement income. What's missing are the intangibles; the thoughts, feelings, and experiences that are at the root of living a truly rewarding retirement. In order to assemble the missing pieces it's important to figure out what's truly important about your time in retirement.

My own epiphany regarding retirement came when I had the opportunity to meet with my first millionaire client. As you can imagine I was excited for the meeting because I was certain it would reveal some enlightening information that would set me on my own path to riches.

During the course of our conversation, I was finally able to ask the million dollar question, "What was the best investment you ever made?"

Retirementality

"I think people's perception of a rich girl is literal, but metaphorically I embrace it as being rich in love, spirit, joy and religion. So it's not about money."

Angie Stone

"No one can serve two masters. Either you will hate the one and love the other, or you will be devoted to the one and despise the other. You cannot serve both God and money."

Mathew 6:24 NIV

Of course, I went into the meeting wondering if she just got lucky in real estate, somehow knew Sam Walton, or had kids with ties to Microsoft and Bill Gates. Which is why I was shocked and extremely disappointed when, without hesitation, she said that the best investment she ever made was, "the Craft-matic Adjustable Bed."

Well, that brought me back down to earth in a hurry. I thought I was going to somehow get rich as a result of this meeting but here I was walking away with nothing more than a product testimonial from a late-night infomercial. I wanted to ask her if she owned the "Clapper," too, since they seem like they would go together.

At the time, I was so focused on money that I didn't much care that her Craft-matic Adjustable Bed gave her a great night sleep. Yet, what I didn't know then, but do now, is that life, at any stage, isn't defined by money, investments, or a net worth, but rather by the Craft-matics - the things you see and do every day that keep you happy and fulfilled.

And that's exactly what we are going to uncover next with our Retirement Foundations questions and worksheet. Answer the following questions in as much detail, and with as much feeling and conviction as possible. This exercise can have a powerful impact on your retirement if you put effort into your answers, and allow what they reveal to work for you.

Spend as much time as you need on each question before moving onto the next section.

RETIREMENT FOUNDATIONS EXERCISE

1 Dare to dream big for a moment. Step away from the confines of traditional retirement planning by removing any preconceived notions or limitations and think big and bold. What's your absolutely perfect retirement? How much money would you love to have saved? How much income will you live on each year? What type of car(s) will you drive? Will you travel? Live in more than one location? What hobbies and leisure activities will you participate in? What will you do with your time? What hopes and dreams have been on hold until retirement? Below, be specific about what your perfect day and perfect week will look like.

Perfect Retirement

_____
_____
_____
_____

Perfect Day In Retirement

Morning:

_____
_____

Afternoon:

_____
_____

Evening:

_____
_____

Perfect Week In Retirement

Sunday: _____

Monday: _____

Tuesday: _____

Wednesday: _____

Thursday: _____

Friday: _____

Saturday: _____

Naked RETIREMENT

2 Imagine that the day after you retire your doctor informs you that you have only five years to live. Stop for a moment and let the emotional impact set in. Your life has just been cut short by 20-30 years, and your ideal retirement has just vanished. Think about how your life will change knowing that your ability to experience and enjoy it will be gone in five short years. Now, what will your focus in retirement be? Describe what you would want to accomplish, see, or do during your final years.

3 Suppose you went back to your doctor and were suddenly informed that you have just 24 hours to live. Instead of concentrating on what you would do with your remaining time, ask yourself, what regrets would you have? What hopes and dreams would go unfulfilled? What do you wish you had accomplished, seen, felt, and experienced in your life now that it is at its end? How will you be remembered? What will your legacy be?

_____

_____

_____

_____

_____

_____

_____

_____

_____

_____

_____

_____

_____

_____

_____

_____

_____

_____

_____

_____

_____

_____

_____

_____

_____

_____

_____

_____

_____

_____

Naked RETIREMENT

Take a minute to think about your answers to these questions and what they brought to light for you What did you come to understand about yourself and what's important to you in retirement? Did your idea of a perfect retirement in Section 1 differ from what you identified as the most essential in Section 3?

This exercise represents the next step in changing your retirement from average to happy, healthy, and connected. Often, when people are asked to define their perfect retirement, their answers are based on things society values and we use to compare and judge each other - a practice that can limit one's personal dreams and desires. Typically, money, possessions, hobbies and things of this nature dominate this area.

But when you focus on the things that are most important to you, the results change from what others value to what you personally value. Ironically, the savings you need for retirement, as well as any anxiety you may have about it, tend to decrease as you shift your focus from what you *think* would make it perfect to what *will* make it meaningful.

This point is highlighted in an interview I had with Pastor Rick Warren, author of the best-selling book *A Purpose Driven Life*. He stated that, "As a pastor, I have stood at the bedside of literally thousands of people as they took their last breath. I have never once had somebody at their dying moment say, 'Bring me my bowling trophy, I want to see it one more time; bring me my certificate, my degree, so I can look at it one more time; bring me the nice gold watch I got for 30 years of service at my company.' Nobody ever says that. They say, 'Bring me the people that I love.' In the closing moments of their life, what people want are those they love the most around them. We all eventually figure out that life is all about love. I just hope people learn that sooner."

Pastor Warren's advice and this exercise also bring one of the major flaws of traditional retirement planning into focus. The idea that you have 20-30 years to do whatever you want with…. to accomplish all the things you expect to get done or experience on your own terms and timeline. Rest assured, however, that's not always the case. The hard reality is, things can change very quickly in retirement, and the only earthly guarantee that comes with it, is that at some point, you will die.

I recently had a client share with me that he was diagnosed with prostate cancer and was receiving radiation treatment for it. That was the good news. In the same month that his wife retired she was also diagnosed with lung cancer and given six months to live. That's a game changer. Retirement immediately took on a distinctly different look and feel than they ever envisioned.

Similarly, there was the case of the chief of police and his wife of 50 years. They had a story book retirement complete with selling their house at a major premium just before the real estate market collapsed in 2007.

They loved to golf, dance, and entertain until she suffered a debilitating stroke. A colossal change that dramatically altered their plans and life in retirement. Most people would agree that doesn't seem fair but, sadly, it happens all the time.

Frankly, questions about our own mortality or physical health seem like the perfect conversations to avoid … and most people do. That's why I want to encourage you to do the exact opposite. Use those conversations as motivating factors instead. Never assume you have unlimited time in retirement to do what you want, when you want, because you may never get the chance.

Give your retirement more meaning by approaching it as if every day could be your last. Get your arms around the essential things, such as spending time with family and friends, giving back, learning new skills, exercising, or immersing yourself in your faith as well as a favorite hobby or passion.

Take a minute, now, to go back and update what your perfect day and week will look like. Then use that updated page to create a No-Regrets Retirement Plan. For those of you who really let the emotional impact set in and drive your answers, I can assure you that you're transforming your retirement!

So let's take a deep breath and move onto some more fun and entertaining work that will help us replace our work identity, fill-our time, and stay connected to family and friends.

Look Before You Leap

Start living on your anticipated retirement income. Whether you retire at 50% or 70% of your pre-retirement income, see if eating out less or scaling back to one car is worth retirement now or better served by working another year and saving more.

Consider taking an extended vacation or leave of absence from work to test the retirement waters. It's a great way to find out if you will enjoy hours of free time and lazy lunches or if you'll desire your structured work schedule.

New habits can take up to 30 days to create. So if you're ideal retirement has you walking everyday, cooking a vegetarian meal once a week, or volunteering for a non-profit, build your base now for an easy transition.

Personal Reflections & Applications

_____

_____

_____

_____

_____

_____

_____

_____

_____

_____

_____

_____

_____

_____

_____

_____

_____

_____

_____

_____

_____

_____

Chapter 5

RETIREMENT CURIOUS & FRIEND LISTS

*T*wo of the biggest issues facing new retirees are 1) what to do with their time and 2) how to leave their career identity behind and re-invent themselves. These two major retirement issues are generally disregarded by traditional retirement planning and contribute significantly to the stress and anxiety many people feel once they retire.

Replacing one's work identity can be particularly difficult. It's an issue because many people confuse who they are with what they do. They love their work and what it provides them in terms of structure, prestige, and focus; but they realize too late that their work can't love them back. A sudden inability to equate what you do with who you are can cause some retirees to lose their sense of purpose and stability. Put another way, it can make you feel lost, bored, and even brokenhearted—a short list of things you don't want retirement to include.

Fear and distress can overtake your life as you're forced to start over and redefine your life's plan and direction. This can cause many retirees to wander aimlessly for years until they come to terms with the need to define their ultimate direction and purpose in retirement.

Retirementality

"We know what we are, but not what we may be."
William Shakespeare

"The best way to find yourself is to lose yourself in the service of others."
Mahatma Ghandi

"Curiosity is one of the most permanent and certain characteristics of a vigorous intellect."
Samuel Johnson

Once an executive was offered an early buyout that would put him into retirement a couple years earlier than expected. The buyout offer was so lucrative, he had to take it or risk losing major increases to his pension and severance pay. With retirement thrust on him earlier than expected, he began to miss his old work life. In an attempt to save his sanity, his wife encouraged him to find a place to volunteer so he signed on with a local charity, ringing a bell in front of a store during the winter holiday season.

During his first shift, a former business acquaintance noticed him and pointedly asked him, "John what are you doing?" The comment struck him as if this charity work was beneath him, and he shouldn't be doing it. When he was asked again, "What are you doing?" John froze and didn't have an answer.

He hadn't yet come to terms with the fact that he no longer ran a million-dollar division, and that his day was no longer filled with the things he did before. The prestige that comes with an expensive suit and tie was gone. He didn't know who he was now that his corporate life was over.

For the first time, no one could tell if he was a wealthy, high-profile decision maker or just a local drunk driver performing mandatory community service. The lesson is, that as long as you let your work define you and rely on what others think and say, the more difficult and empty retirement will be.

Frankly, this is exactly what retirees can't afford to do: Become consumed by the negative aspects of their retirement instead of counting their blessings.

Curious List

To help address this identity replacement issue, and fill some newfound time, new and existing retirees should develop a "curious list." A curious list is exactly what it sounds like, a list of things you are interested in and, at some point during retirement, would like to consider learning more about.

RETIREMENT CURIOUS & FRIEND LISTS

What makes the curious list different from a "bucket list" or "honey-do list" is the fact that it does not require a specific commitment of time or energy. Instead, it simply denotes that you wish to spend some amount of time and energy at some point in the future exploring a particular subject.

For example, you could be curious about sky diving, but that doesn't mean you have to do it. You could simply read a book about it, watch a documentary on it, or talk one of your friends into taking the jump.

The secret of the curious list lies in the fact that it creates a desire to do more, be more, or learn more. When you are curious about something you want to take that next step and see what's around the corner. Through small and simple steps you'll not only help build momentum in areas of interest but also gain useful insights, foster experience, and ultimately add energy and direction to your new life. All crucial elements to cultivating a new identity and filling your time with meaningful tasks.

With the worksheet at the end of the chapter, take five minutes to write down as many things as possible that you are curious about. If you have a hard time getting started, or get stuck, there is a list of examples at the bottom of the page that should trigger some responses. Think quietly before you begin, "What do I really want to see myself doing or being a part of in retirement?"

Upon completion, consider adding "investing" to your list. Not because it will turn you into the next Warren Buffet or Wall Street whiz but being curious about investing can help you protect yourself and your family against fraud and bad financial advice. Remember, *No One Cares More About Your Money Than You*, and once you embrace that philosophy, your relationship with money and your advisor will change forever.

A good curious list will support a balanced retirement that incorporates mental and physical health, social activities, financial well-being, and spiritual growth. It will also go a long way in helping new and soon-to-be retires avoid any regrets about their decision to retire.

Friend List

During retirement, we all need human connections for physical, emotional, and spiritual health. Yet, most pre-retirees don't realize that once they are retired, the luxury of running into and connecting with people they know will suddenly and dramatically change.

Research suggests that while working you may have up to 22 high quality (face-to-face) interactions with people on a daily basis. When people retire, that number can get cut in half, to 11, and those interactions are generally of lesser quality because they are more likely to be by phone or email rather than face-to-face. That's a change many people aren't prepared for and one that can leave them feeling isolated or out-of-the-loop.

---

4 Things To Take When You Retire

Business Card & Name Plaque
Keep your name plate and a couple b-cards as a memento of the time, energy and effort you put into your career.

Memberships
If you're part of a work-affiliated association or group, keep paying your dues so you can stay abreast of industry changes and trends.

Pay Stub
Think of your pay stub as your career report card. Keep a few to show your kids and grand kids what it takes to succeed in the workplace.

Contact Info
You never know when you may need a reference and having quick access to a list of people that can vouch for you will save you both time and energy.

Naked RETIREMENT

Sudden Retirement

Whether brought on by a buyout, company closing, or job elimination, a forced retirement is a growing reality among baby boomers.

Sad reality is, it can be just as scary and troubling as a divorce or the loss of a loved one which means it can require patience, personal and professional support, as well as flexibility in adjusting to it.

In 2010 , 41% of retirees stopped working earlier than they expected.

The most common reasons being poor health (54%), corporate downsizing or closures (37%), and the need to care for a spouse or family member (19%).

Source: Employee Benefit Research Institute (EBRI)

Fact is, many adults have not taken the time to look at who they surround themselves with or the impact others can have on their happiness in retirement. We all have that Debbie Downer friend who, as soon as you ask, *"How are things going?"* launches into a 15 minute tirade about how terrible life and the world are. How many times have you had to fake a bad connection, or ring your own doorbell, to get out of such a discouraging conversation?

Reality is, you can't be responsible for someone else's happiness and the people with whom you surround yourself with can have a profound impact on your mood and attitude.

On the other hand, we all have that friend who constantly has a smile on their face, a kind word, or lending hand. They light up a room when they walk in and always make you feel welcomed. So, as you transition into retirement, it's important to think about who you are going to surround yourself with, and how those people affect you.

One Harvard study suggests that your odds of being happy increase by 15% if a direct connection in your network of friends is also happy. Even indirect connections, like having a happy friend of a friend, can increase your chances of being happy by as much as 10%. That may not seem like a big increase but the same study also reveals that an increase in annual income of approximately $10,000 was associated with just a 2% increase in the likelihood of being happy.

With this in mind, take a few minutes with the Friend List section of the worksheet to write down as many happy, vibrant, and energizing people you know. Think about people you like being around, who always make you laugh or smile, and share mutual interests with you.

Finally, when you're done, take a couple minutes to connect the people on your friends list with items on your curious list. Draw a line between the two groups where there may be a link, desire, or opportunity for a shared experience or interest with a friend. Try to build an eventual list of at least 15-20 curious items with 10 or more family members and friends with whom you see opportunities to explore new experiences.

This is an important exercise because it identifies who you want in your circle of influence, who you want to grow and learn with, who will pick you up when you're down, and who you can count on to help you stay connected.

However, don't just put a name on the list and assume they, in turn, know how you feel about them. Make a commitment today to reach out to these people. Let them know what their friendship means to you.

Regardless of whether you call them, email them, or send them a Facebook message, strengthen those relationships now. No one will get upset over receiving a message that says "you're a good friend and I want you to know you're someone I value and want to continue our friendship well into retirement."

Introspective View

On the surface, it seems easy to assess other people's friendships, moods and attitudes, which is why it's important to examine your own as well. We all need people in our lives who will be caring, supportive, candid, reliable and committed. But there is only one way you're going to get people like this in your life: You have to be that kind of friend first. Ask yourself, "Would somebody put me on their friends list?" Why or why not?

Take a moment to think about what makes for a good friendship: Consider things like reaching out to them on a regular basis, sharing with them what's going in in your life, and investing time and energy into things they care about and enjoy.

Together, the curious and friendship lists provide a key for unlocking barriers to replacing your work identity, filling your time with more meaningful things, and staying connected to happy, energetic people. It's a powerful combination that will move you another step closer to a remarkable retirement.

Retirementality

"Walking with a friend in the dark is better than walking alone in the light."
Helen Keller

"Two people are better off than one, for they can help each other succeed. If one person falls, the other can reach out and help. But someone who falls alone is in real trouble."
Ecclesiastes 4:9-10

RETIREMENT CURIOUS & FRIEND LISTS

Curious List	Friend List
1)	
2)	
3)	
4)	
5)	
6)	
7)	
8)	
9)	
10)	
11)	
12)	
13)	
14)	
15)	

Curious List Examples:

Writing a book	Religion/The Bible	Scuba diving
Skydiving	Your grandchildren	Family tree
Painting	Theatre	Choir
Musical instrument	Second language	Foreign culture
Song writing	Horseback riding	Sailing
Sign language	Special needs children	Dancing
Economics	Computers	Card games
Safari	Hot air balloons	Classic cars
Antiques	Foreign country	Gardening
Sporting events/teams	Museums	Airplanes
Magic	Whale watching	Cold case files

Personal Reflections & Applications

_____
_____
_____
_____
_____
_____
_____
_____
_____
_____
_____
_____
_____
_____
_____
_____
_____
_____
_____
_____
_____
_____

Chapter 6

RETIREMENT WELL-BEING

RETIREMENT WELL-BEING

Naked RETIREMENT

A good deal of our ability to prosper in our retirement years is dependent on keeping our bodies, mind and spirit healthy. Many retirees may be prepared for the financial aspects of their golden years, but they don't have an exercise routine, nutritional guidelines, or strategies to avoid boredom, bad habits, or losing one or more of their five senses. People are living longer nowadays, but that doesn't necessarily mean they will remain active and inspired during those additional years… and all the freedom and money in the world won't change that.

Retirementality

"To keep the body in good health is a duty… otherwise we shall not be able to keep our mind strong and clear."

Buddha

"It takes more than just a good looking body. You've got to have the heart and soul to go with it."

Epictetus

"Do you not know that you are God's temple and that God's Spirit dwells in you? If anyone destroys God's temple, God will destroy him. For God's temple is holy, and you are that temple."

1 Corinthians 3:16-17 ESV

In fact, most people don't realize that retirement only magnifies what you already are, particularly when it comes to health. If you frequent the couch, prefer fatty foods, or are always trying to please others, retirement will only provide more time to reinforce those habits.

That's why it's important to take as much care of your health as you do your wealth, because the best legacy you can give your family is a faithful and healthy you. Therefore, in addition to knowing how much you need to save, how your assets should be allocated, and how much you can withdraw each year, make sure you consistently monitor numbers like these as well:

- Cholesterol level
- Fasting blood sugar level
- Body mass index (BMI)
- Blood pressure
- Resting heart rate

Measures of health like these are important because it's easy to let exercise and eating habits slip once you retire. Now I'm not suggesting that retirees don't deserve some down time after working for 30 or 40 years, but it's important to balance rest with healthy activities in order to avoid getting too sedentary.

I think it's also important to note that taking control of your health in retirement doesn't mean you have to spend hours in the gym and sweat your way back to how you looked at 25. Nor does it mean that you have to rely on your own will power, starve yourself, or use pills to alter your appearance.

Just as we are redefining your thoughts and ideas about retirement, a similar change is necessary when it comes to getting healthy in retirement. Don't rely on your own knowledge or past experiences. Seek out the gifts and skills of local fitness professionals and culinary experts that will keep you functional and fun, not famished and weary.

Retirement well-being is not only about your physical health and what you're eating, but also what might be eating you? If your body and soul are filled with fear, resentment, worry, guilt, anger or other emotional issues, it will show up in your physical appearance and your behavior.

RETIREMENT WELL-BEING

Emotional health requires that you have time to yourself and the space in your life to adapt to what's happening. Being overwhelmed or stressed out can leave you feeling inadequate and easy to anger around your loved ones.

Therefore, just as you would sign up for an exercise class or set a regular workout schedule, set time aside everyday to rest your mind and connect with God. Like many other things in life, finding inner peace takes time, energy, and effort.

In addition to helping you create a health plan to keep your body and mind strong, in motion, and protected against common disease, I also want to make you more aware of health factors that aren't often talked about, like losing one of your five senses such as vision or hearing.

I recently learned that a client had to surrender her driver's license. At just 67, her optometrist was unable to provide the script she needed together license renewed because of her declining peripheral vision. A bitter pill to swallow for a single woman living on the outskirts of town with few family and friends close by to drive her around.

With only a local shuttle service available, a simple trip to the grocery store now takes her over 5 hours. I can assure you that no one goes into retirement dreaming of a five hour bus trip just to buy a few groceries, or being dependent on family and friends to ferry them around.

Similarly, another client said he had over fifty family members and friends at his house over the holidays. You might consider that a blessing but he complained bitterly that his hearing has declined to such an extent he can no longer participate in group discussions. Thus, he felt isolated and out of touch in his own home even though he was surrounded by people he loves and who love him.

On the surface, these situations may seem disheartening but you have to be prepared to adjust your retirement to life's direction. Instead of fighting the changes, embrace them as it may just be time to focus on a few important relationships instead of many or move closer to town in order to easily access the things you want and need.

Whether it's the loss of an important sense, your physical body, or mental capacity, the best strategy to combat their decline is to maintain a healthy, active mindset and lifestyle.

Therefore, use the Retirement Well-Being section on the next page to highlight 1) healthy habits you'd like to start or continue 2) health opportunities such as things you want to see, hear, and do on your own or as part of a group; and 3) health concerns which can include aspects of your family health history that you should begin to address.

---

2 Things To Do Before You Retire

Eat A Great Meal
Whether its lobster, filet mignon, or some other delicacy, make it an annual tradition to eat a meal that's good enough to be your last. Stimulate your taste buds in a way you'll never forget as you celebrate the finer things in life.

Take More Pictures
Those who stay socially engaged with others and who have a strong network of friends tend to live longer.

Therefore, one simple ways to connect with old and new friends is through pictures. Simply ask for their email or Facebook I.D. and offer to send them copies of photos or tag them in it.

It's a proven way to create lasting memories as well as new relationships.

RETIREMENT WELL-BEING

#1 Healthy Habits:

Identify three health-related _habits_ you plan to continue or start in retirement. For example: walking, biking, swimming, taking vitamins, eating vegetarian, eliminating gluten from your diet, eating more fruits and vegetables, cooking a healthy meal once a week, etc.

1) _____

2) _____

3) _____

#2 Health Opportunities:

Identify three health-related _opportunities_ that you plan to take advantage of in retirement, including things you may want to see, speak about, hear, smell, or touch. For example: Take a healthy cooking class, join a gym, sign up for a yoga class, learn or teach CPR, partake in a physically challenging adventure, see a championship sporting event, hear the roar of Niagara Falls, taste a fine wine, feel the warmth of a camp fire, savor the smell of a new car.

1) _____

2) _____

3) _____

#3 Health Concerns:

Everybody knows you can pick your friends but you can't pick your family. Obviously, this means you can't avoid your family's medical history, or conditions passed on through the genes. Whether its high blood pressure, cholesterol, heart condition, cancer, weight, alcoholism, diabetes, etc., identify three health-related _concerns_ that you need to stay on top of and combat with healthy habits.

1) _____

2) _____

3) _____

Living a rewarding retirement means being active, involved, and knowing your health numbers … not to mention taking care of your five senses. Developing and maintaining a healthy retirement lifestyle contributes to your retirement identity, can help you stay socially involved, fill your time, stave off boredom and keep you from slipping into the dark side of retirement.

Remember, the real foundation for wealth is your complete and total health. Therefore, today's comprehensive retirement plan requires putting "how much you need to save" behind "the numbers and activities you need to stay alive."

Personal Reflections & Applications

Chapter 7

RETIREMENT CONVERSATIONS

RETIREMENT CONVERSATIONS

D uring one of my workshops, a single woman shared with me that she was getting ready to retire and told a friend at work about her plans. Instead of a hug or simple congratulation, her friend appeared annoyed and remarked, "Well, if you still want to meet or get together you'll have make the arrangements and travel here to meet with me." I wasn't totally surprised by this response but many of you may be tempted to ask "what kind of friends does she have?"

In another workshop, a woman famously told her husband, "I married you for better or worse but not for lunch every day." Surprisingly, many couples are not on the same page when it comes to retirement, including whether or not they will eat every meal together or go separate ways on certain days and times.

> ## *Retirementality*
>
> *"You can make positive deposits in your own economy every day by reading and listening to powerful, positive, life-changing content and by associating with encouraging and hope-building people."*
>
> Zig Zigler
>
> *"To answer before listening - that is folly and shame."*
>
> Proverbs 18:13 NIV

Reality is, everyday life in retirement comes with its own stereotypes and assumptions. People may imagine how it's going to work, but aren't always effective in communicating those thoughts, which is exactly where danger lurks. If, for example, assumptions about how you'll spend your time, levels of family involvement, spiritual commitment, relationships needs, and household responsibilities aren't addressed before you retire, they can become points of contention and conflict throughout retirement.

Many of these potentially damaging assumptions and stereotypes can be resolved with proactive discussions about retirement before you actually make the big move. Investing the time to do so will establish an open and consistent approach to resolving issues and making decisions before they become a problem. The following questions about retirement can serve as topics of conversation to be discussed with family, friends, and colleagues. Use them to initiate conversations, gauge expectations, and to build a meaningful approach to your relationships in retirement.

Words are powerful, so be mindful of what you say and how you say it during these discussions. Differing views and opinions can intensify matters and make your time in retirement more tense and emotionally draining than it needs to be. Therefore, be patient, and "seek first to understand than to be understood."

It's important to point out that you do not have to go through and answer every single question. The goal was to develop an extensive list that you could use to identify important topics as well as areas of retirement that you may not have thought about before.

At the end of the questions, there is a worksheet that allows you to organize your most important conversations, the people you need to have them with, and a time frame within which to have them. Whether, you're ten days or ten years away from retirement, start these conversations now instead of putting them off until later.

<u>Retirement Questions</u>

What does your job provide that you will miss in retirement? Think about the mental, social, and physical aspects of your work. What steps can you take to maintain or replace them?

What skills and talents do you have and how do you plan to continue to use them? Make a list.

Once you retire, you will no longer have a work identity. How will you identify yourself when you meet new people? When was the last time you were introduced to, or met, a retiree? What was your first impression of that person? How did they, in turn, refer to themselves?

What will you do with your time during retirement? How will the way you plan to spend time affect your relationships with others? What relationships may benefit; which ones, including previous work relationships, may need some preservation work? In your recent past, what jobs or leisure activities have you most enjoyed?

If you're married, will you go to bed and wake up at the same time? Will you eat breakfast, lunch, and dinner together every day? How much alone time will each of you need? What spiritual commitments will you seek together as well as independently?

What discussions should you begin having with your spouse, siblings, or your parents if you retire before they do? What impact is that likely to have on your relationship with them? What household expectations may change?

How will you relate to, and interact with, friends who are still working? To what degree would moving or spending time in a distant location affect family relationships and friendships?

How will your retirement affect family members? Will there be more or less visiting? What role will you play with your grandkids? Is everyone in agreement on this? How will you communicate your plans to your family?

What blessings do you need to count and thank God for? Do you have a spiritual plan? Will you set specific time(s) aside for worship including church attendance or Bible study?

Which monthly bills and regular expenses will change? Will any expenses be eliminated; will any be added? How will healthcare costs figure into your retirement budget? Will you continue to save during retirement? What about tithing, giving to charity, or gifting to children or grandchildren?

What major expenses do you anticipate in retirement? Consider new vehicles, home updates, travel, helping out family or friends, etc.

Do family, friends, or organizations anticipate an inheritance from your estate? What conflicts might arise among heirs? If you have a blended family, how will assets and possessions be used and divided? What personal and spiritual traditions do you want to pass on and be remembered for?

Are there any thoughts, questions, or concerns about retiring that keep you awake at night? Specifically, under what circumstances would you outlive your money? If you ran out of money, who would you ask for help?

Would the time, energy, or cost of supporting an adult child, grandchild, or parent have a bearing on your retirement budget or lifestyle? Are some family members more likely than others to ask for money, or move in with you? Have you established ground rules governing how you will help, or how modified living arrangements might work?

If you had to return to work, what kind of jobs would best utilize your strengths? What types of work would be most fulfilling?

During retirement, which activities and people are likely to give you the best return on the time, energy, and the money you invest in them?

What role will your physical and mental health play during your retirement? Do you anticipate that your current mental and physical health will impact your daily living, sex life, diet, and healthcare costs?

RETIREMENT CONVERSATIONS

What is the one thing you hope no one finds out about your current retirement plan? What retirement conversations are you avoiding?

Retirement Conversations	Person(s)	Time Frame

By proactively discussing your thoughts and plans for everyday life in retirement you can avoid dangerous assumptions that can lead to years of arguments and, ultimately, living a less-than meaningful retirement. Preemptive conversations strengthen not only your communication skills but more importantly, the relationships that mean the most to you.

Since these issues are often overlooked and seldom planned for, don't be caught off guard if a family member, friend, or colleague seems confused about what retirement means to you. Be prepared to explain how you plan to spend your time in retirement, and make it clear that you're retiring from your job, not from life or your relationship with them.

Personal Reflections & Applications

_____

_____

_____

_____

_____

_____

_____

_____

_____

_____

_____

_____

_____

_____

_____

_____

_____

_____

_____

_____

_____

_____

_____

_____

Chapter 8
SPIRITUAL RETIREMENT

SPIRITUAL RETIREMENT

*T*he idea of a spiritual retirement can carry with it a variety of connotations. It's generally a taboo subject that few planners and clients ever address simply because there's no guidebook or suggestions on how to best cover this topic. But I think it's important to break the ice and start talking about it. I want to be clear upfront, that I'm not looking to debate religion, sign anyone up for a church committee, or post a list of *Thou Shall Not's*.

Instead, I want to push the bounds of retirement conversations and plans by addressing it simply because no matter how you define spirituality, it is a real aspect of retirement that shouldn't be avoided or ignored.

Throughout this book, I have shared many personal stories that shaped my view of retirement and my desire to help people see it in a different light. Well, the same holds true for the spiritual aspects. I was done with a revision of the book when I asked a friend to review it for me. A couple weeks later we met for lunch and I asked for his feedback. I was hoping he'd say he submitted it for Pulitzer Prize consideration, or at least brought in a flash mob to applaud my efforts. Neither happened. However, his perspective pushed my thoughts and comfort level for the book to a new level. After some casual conversation, he politely said, "You're book is very good but misses an important point. It assumes that retirement is life's ultimate reward and end point, but it's not. Getting into heaven is."

I realized immediately that most traditional retirement plans address life up-to-death through life insurance and various estate planning techniques to create a financial legacy and ensure minimal taxation. However, what I see missing is one of the most important retirement questions all of us face: Where and how do I plan to spend eternity?

Retirementality

"The greatest disease in the West today is not TB or leprosy; it is being unwanted, unloved, and uncared for. We can cure physical diseases with medicine, but the only cure for loneliness, despair, and hopelessness is love."

Mother Teresa

"Just as a candle cannot burn without fire, men cannot live without a spiritual life."

Buddha

That's deep and spiritually moving... to some. However, this is a taboo topic and not everyone agrees. The very same week I had a discussion with another friend about adding a spiritual chapter and he commented "Whatever you do, don't ruin your book by putting anything about God in there."

I can say, that level of divergence was a sign to find a way to open up the conversation. The hard part, of course, is how to do it in a way that doesn't offend some, cause their defenses to go up..

So I started having more conversations with clients, family and friends. What's been interesting, but not totally surprising, is that like other areas of retirement, most people had some thoughts and ideas in their heads yet hadn't taken the crucial step of writing them down and discussing them with others.

For example, during one conversation, I asked a friend if he believed in God. He forcefully responded, "Well how do you define God? If it's some white guy with a beard, sitting on a golden thrown resting in the clouds, then no I don't." It was a reminder of just how delicate such conversations can be. Eventually, I was able to say that I wasn't asking him to use my definition or someone else's interpretation, but rather if he had a belief and definition of his own.

SPIRITUAL RETIREMENT

Throughout the book, my goal has been to push you to develop your own vision for retirement. To ditch the media or mainstream images and ideas, and create your own more personal approach. The same holds true for this chapter and topic, even if it is taboo. Remember from the last chapter, words are powerful, so be mindful of what you say and how you say it. This is not the time or place to convince someone else of your beliefs or judge their spiritual walk.

Do you believe in God or a higher power? Why or why not? How would you describe your relationship? How have you come to this point in your spiritual journey?

Is there life after death? A heaven or hell? If so, how do you define them?

Are your beliefs independent or do others follow the same path? Do you read, follow, or subscribe to religious texts, rules or commandments? If so, how closely do you adhere to them?

As you might expect, these answers can vary from person-to-person as well as situation-to-situation. For me, I grew up Catholic but stepped away from my faith after my parents divorced; further distancing myself in college when I began reading world history and other religious texts.

It actually wasn't until a few years ago that I recommitted to the Christian faith. I had definitely used supernatural events like Jesus walking on water, the Virgin Mary, and resurrection as reasons not to believe, that is until I found myself in a bad situation. Then I was suddenly a believer and praying for help.

My spiritual life changed when I made a commitment to start looking for reasons to believe instead of using my own logic to avoid church and the way I was brought up. Looking back at my past, there are probably a few people who would say my salvation is more supernatural than many of the Bible's other miracles.

Retirement Lessons From the Bible

For those who enter retirement unprepared for everything it is, they can look to the story of Abraham who at age 75 was told by God to leave behind his comforts - and everything he knew - for an unknown destination.

For others who may have been forced into retirement because of corporate downsizing, a health problem, or other unexpected circumstance, they can learn from Daniel's unwavering faith as he overcame the Lion's Den after being betrayed by his co-workers.

Even those who think they are prepared and called by God to take their life in a new direction, can garner retirement lessons from the many trials and tribulations the Apostle Paul faced after Jesus called out to him on the road to Damascus.

In each case, the lives of Abraham, Daniel, and Paul all grew brighter as they pursued their faith and their relationship with God.

SPIRITUAL RETIREMENT

Naked RETIREMENT

In any event, I can share with you that as I have studied retirement and re-established my own faith, I have been inspired by the fact that every premise in this book has a foundation in the Bible. I wish I could say that I came up with them all on my own, but whether it's the importance of family and friends, taking care of your body and mind, watching what you say to others, or using your skills and talents, each concept is literally thousands of years old, and carries with it the same significance today as it did back then. Ironically though, the Bible only references the term "retire" once and it's short and limited in scope when compared to the choices, opportunities, and challenges faced by today's retirees.

> *"The LORD said to Moses, [24] 'This applies to the Levites: Men twenty-five years old or more shall come to take part in the work at the tent of meeting, [25] but at the age of fifty, they must retire from their regular service and work no longer. [26] They may assist their brothers in performing their duties at the tent of meeting, but they themselves must not do the work. This, then, is how you are to assign the responsibilities of the Levites.'" Numbers 8:23-26 NIV*

Bible verses like these are the things that can get taken out of perspective and end up being applied out of context. On the surface, it would appear that this passage leaves the topic of retirement fairly open to interpretation. That in some cases, you can stop working at 50 and bark out orders from a lounge chair.

Fact of the matter is, the Bible doesn't endorse the way many people perceive retirement. Nowhere does scripture offer ideas or suggestions for living a leisure filled, self-serving life. There's no extra commandments or prophet that says you can sit on the couch all day, let your relationship deteriorate, give up on your health and well-being, stop using your gifts and talents, and most of all stop serving others. That being said, you're not going to end up in hell because you accepted a buy-out offer or decided 35 years with the same company was enough.

The challenge comes in when people turn retirement into a selfish time where they can do, say, or be whatever they want, without limitation or consequence. No matter what spiritual path you follow, universal concepts like loving and helping others can make retirement more meaningful... which is why I believe it's important to put yourself in situations and surround yourself with others of like mind and spirit. Otherwise retirement can become a one-way street where some retirees feel they are the sun instead of a planet working in concert with others.

While the Bible doesn't endorse many of today's retirement ideals, I feel decisions about whether or not you want to develop a spiritual aspect to your retirement is best exemplified by comparing your retirement voyage on two very popular, yet very different ships: Noah's Ark and The Titanic. As you know, *professionals* built the Titanic and claimed it was unsinkable, while others mocked an amateur as he built the Ark.

SPIRITUAL RETIREMENT

Without knowing the eventual result, the big, shiny ship may look like the perfect place to start and enjoy your retirement years, but when you consider how both ended up, little doubt exists as to the possibilities a retirement voyage with a spiritual component could have for you.

Unfortunately today, many people are just focused on the time and money they have on earth, and unknowingly preparing for a voyage on the Titanic: A journey that may never offer true happiness, just as the ship never settled into a port. That's why I think it's important to stop conforming to mainstream ideas and views about retirement and start discussing taboo subjects like this.

Consider adding a deeper spiritual element to the work you have done so far by taking a moment to answer the following questions.

What disturbs you? What distresses your heart and causes you to think, 'I need to do something about that'? What organizations and people can help you make an impact in others' lives?

Are there temptations that may pose as a major threat to you and your family during retirement?

Questions can sometimes be the answer. Are there any faith-based questions or opportunities you'd like to add to your curious list?

Is there someone you need to forgive and wipe the slate clean with? Is there something you need to forgive yourself for?

What impact might a deeper, more committed spiritual relationship have on family, friends, and those in your community?

Are there conversations you need to have with God?

Where do you plan to spend eternity?

Personal Reflections & Applications

_____

_____

_____

_____

_____

_____

_____

_____

_____

_____

_____

_____

_____

_____

_____

_____

_____

_____

_____

_____

_____

_____

Chapter 9

NAKED RETIREMENT PLAN

Naked RETIREMENT PLAN

Naked Retirement was created as a way to help people re-envision retirement planning in a more personal and meaningful way. To assist them in developing and applying a level of retirement readiness that goes beyond just the dollars and cents to include the mental, social, physical, and spiritual aspects.

Many pre-retirees start out looking at retirement through a broken lens. A distorted view that tends to focus more on money than the individual. However, by going through the *Naked Retirement* program, you have created a more personalized outlook through which you can see retirement in a completely different light. In the end, you will have eloquently positioned yourself to live and experience retirement to its fullest.

Fact is, you've done some amazing work by completing the *Naked Retirement* exercises. The Retirement Perceptions Quiz, for example, has turned your initial views and ideas about retirement into new realities … everyday realities that help you avoid stress and make the most of your newly discovered opportunities.

You've uncovered your "Craft-matics" … the things that make you feel happy and fulfilled each and every day. You have a list of things you're curious about, which will help you replace your work identity and fill your time. A list of friends to keep you happy and connected, health goals that can play a major part in helping you live a long and active retirement… and the spiritual capacity to call on, and work through God, during both the good times and challenging moments. These are all vital ingredients to both a successful retirement and a prosperous life leading up to it.

Retirementality

"His master replied, 'Well done, good and faithful servant! You have been faithful with a few things; I will put you in charge of many things. Come and share your master's happiness!'"

Matthew 25:21 NIV

"I need to retire from retirement."

Sandra Day O'Connor

What I have learned over the years about retirement is that it's empty! Meaning, it's completely up to you to fill it with what you desire and with all the things that allow you to live a no-regrets retirement.

Retirement is also privilege that many people never get to experience. So approach it with great respect and be grateful for the opportunities it presents. Finally, bear in mind that retirement is not automatic; it doesn't just happen. It takes time, energy, planning like this, and practice to make it the best it can be.

Your final *Naked Retirement* exercise is to crystallize your brand new thoughts, ideas, and beliefs by creating a one-page *Naked Retirement Plan*. This will become your personal reference point to which you can regularly revisit for guidance on the mental, social, physical and spiritual aspects of retirement.

Each section will help you create a balanced approach to retirement with specific ideas for dealing with the many issues that are not addressed in traditional retirement planning. On following page is a list of instructions to help you complete the Naked Retirement Plan at the end of the chapter.

1: Retirement Bumper Sticker
The first part of your final exercise is to create a retirement bumper sticker, or a mantra, that summarizes your new thoughts and feelings about retirement. Construct it using keywords, memorable phrase, or acronym that reflects something that stuck with you after completing one of the exercises. It might be something from your curious list, friends list, or simply a top-of-mind impression you have. For example, create a catchphrase such as *Free at last!* or *No more alarm clock!* Make it an acronym such as *NRR!* for *No Regrets Retirement*, or use your favorite Bible verse.

2: Things I Believe About Retirement
Next, imagine for a moment that you were asked to tell a room full of people what you believe about retirement. What would you say or compare it to? What does it offer you? Record 3-5 core beliefs in the space provided and use them in conversations to establish good expectations for what life in retirement means to you.

3: Top Five Curious List Items
Review your entire curious list and select your top five. List them in order of interest.

4: Retirement Conversations
Review your answers from the Retirement Conversations worksheet. Select the five most important conversations you need to have and list them here along with the target person to have the discussion with and timeframe for each conversation.

5: Wealth Concerns
While we didn't spend any time of the topic, there is the financial component to retirement that you need to consider. Take some time to write down any financial concerns you may have such as, How do I know if I can trust an advisor? Which pension option should I consider? Should I have gold and silver in my portfolio? Should I own bonds given the current interest rate environment and, if so, what kinds? What should I ask them, and how can I research them? Can I pay a professional to review my investments without being pressured to buy a product?

6: Health Habits, Opportunities, and Concerns
Similar to the top five curious list items, list 3-5 health habits, opportunities, or concerns that you want to address immediately.

7: Spiritual Action Plan
In the end, when your number is finally called, you can't take your money or any earthly possessions with you. Therefore, make a real and lasting commitment to do something with all the work you have just completed. Take a moment to listen to what's on your heart and in your mind. Then write down a minimum of three to five actions you will take in the next week … and commit to them. It could be to calling a friend from your friends list; or contacting a local adult education program to sign up for a class in piano playing, yoga, or sign language. Maybe you'd like to pick up your Bible again, or just take the first step toward something you're feeling compelled to do. Whatever the decision, use this section of the plan to start creating a more meaningful retirement right now.

Hang your completed list where you will see it every day. Use it to stay connected with your vision for retirement and conscious of the fact that money can't buy great friends, good health, or a happy ending, but a little planning on the everyday aspects of retirement can help you make the most of it.

Thank you for letting *Naked Retirement* be your guide and for placing your trust in the program. I hope your thoughts and plans about retirement have been dramatically transformed and that the work you've done helps you live a happy, healthy, and connected retirement.

Retirementality

"When I stand before God at the end of my life, I would hope that I would not have a single bit of talent left, and could say, 'I used everything you gave me.'"
Erma Bombeck

"Only a life lived for others is a life worthwhile."
Albert Einstein

"Go confidently in the direction of your dreams. Live the life you have imagined."

Henry David Thoreau

"The Lord himself goes before you and will be with you; he will never leave you nor forsake you. Do not be afraid; do not be discouraged."
Deuteronomy 31:8 NIV

"What good is it for a man to gain the whole world, yet forfeit his soul?"
Mark 8:36 NIV

Naked RETIREMENT PLAN

1: Retirement Bumper Sticker

_____
_____

2: What I Believe About Retirement

1) _____
2) _____
3) _____
4) _____
5) _____

3: Top Five Curious List Items

1) _____
2) _____
3) _____
4) _____
5) _____

4: Retirement Conversations	Person(s)	Time Frame
_____	_____	_____
_____	_____	_____
_____	_____	_____
_____	_____	_____
_____	_____	_____

5: Wealth Concerns & Opportunities

1) _____ 2) _____ 3) _____

6: Health Habits, Opportunities, and Issues

1) _____
2) _____
3) _____
4) _____
5) _____

7: Spiritual Action Plan

1) _____
2) _____
3) _____
4) _____
5) _____

Personal Reflections & Applications

_____
_____
_____
_____
_____
_____
_____
_____
_____
_____
_____
_____
_____
_____
_____
_____
_____
_____
_____
_____
_____
_____
_____

Personal Reflections & Applications

_____
_____
_____
_____
_____
_____
_____
_____
_____
_____
_____
_____
_____
_____
_____
_____
_____
_____
_____
_____
_____
_____
_____
_____
_____
_____
_____

SOURCES

Source Information

Chapter 1: Retirement Reality
Adapted from Anthony Robbins, Awaken The Giant Within (New York: Fireside / Simon & Schuster 1991) p.241.

Chapter 2: Retirement Perceptions
Retirement study: Forbes.com, Can Your Marriage Survive Retirement, by Robert Laura, quoting Rob Pascale PhD, January 2013.

Chapter 3: Retirement Dark Side
Chilling RX: The New York Times; "Addicts of A Certain Age: Baby Boomers Need Help." March 6, 2008.

Chapter 4: Retirement Foundations:
Adapted from George Kinder, Seven Stages of Money Maturity, Dell Publishing, a division of Random House, copyright 1999, p.154.156, 158.

Chapter 4: Retirement Foundations:
Rick Warren: Forbes.com, Pastor Rick Warren Is Well prepared For A Purpose Driven Retirement, by Robert Laura, March 2013.

Chapter 5: Retirement Curious &Friend Lists
Harvard Study, The Five Essential Elements by Tom Rath, Jim Harter, P.17Gallup press, 2010, Adapted from Clark, et, al, The Economic Journal, June 2008.

Chapter 5: Retirement Curious &Friend Lists
Communication Research: Forbes.com, interview with Rob Pascale PhD, January 2013.

ABOUT THE AUTHOR

Robert Laura is a best-selling author and nationally syndicated columnist for Forbes.com and Financial Advisor Magazine. His work has reached more than 5,000,000 readers through five books, twelve guides, and over 500 articles. In addition to his own writings, he frequently appears in major business media outlets such as the Wall Street Journal, USA Today, CNBC, MarketWatch, Investor's Business Daily, Yahoo! Finance, TheStreet.com, and more.

Robert is the founder of the Wealth & Wellness Group, the RetirementProject.org and Certified Retirement Coach Designation. He holds several designations including Accredited Asset Management Specialist, Certified Mutual Fund Counselor, Chartered Retirement Planning Counselor, Certified Kingdom Advisor, and Certified Professional Retirement Coach. He is a pioneer in the psychology and social science of retirement planning, and showcases the knowledge and skill as a 15-year veteran of the National Speakers Association and a frequent presenter at retirement conferences across the country.

He has a garnered a unique look at wealth and retirement by not only working closely with his own clients for the last twenty years, but also by interviewing numerous celebrities, entertainers, and athletes including Pastor Rick Warren, Deion Sanders, John Sally, Gymnast Shannon Miller, Golfer Annika Sorenstam, Singer Amy Grant, HGTV's the Property Brothers, Pawn Star Rick Harrison, Impersonator Rich Little and more. This work reflects his ground-breaking efforts to challenge the status quo of traditional retirement planning and help people create a No-Regrets Retirement Plan!

Robert has been a speaking and teaching retirement based programs for two decades. His presentations are ideal for every group, from business owners and executives to employees, associations, and senior citizens. His charismatic and humorous style allows his audiences to get educated in an entertaining way as he creates a memorable experience that touches both the mind and the heart. With thought-provoking insights, vivid stories, and a frequent dose of humor, he reaches audiences in a way they do not forget.

THE RETIREMENT PROJECT

Retirement Project is an educational initiative designed to help people plan for everyday life in retirement. Our belief is that retirement planning can no longer focus solely on the dollars and cents. It has to include specific planning for the mental, social, physical, and spiritual aspects of life in retirement. Things such as how you will replace your work identity, fill your time, stay connected to family and friends, as well as physically fit.

We have found that retirement is among the most fascinating, yet least understood, phases of life. Therefore, we are committed to changing the way people think about and prepare for every aspect of retirement by challenging the status quo of it. Our goal is simple: We want to help you create a "No Regrets" retirement life and plan!

Visit RetirementProject.org

Made in United States
Troutdale, OR
07/21/2023

11460173R00035